A Biblical Approach to

InSideOut COACHING

By Joe Ehrmann
with Paula Ehrmann
and Mark Hull

Biblical Approach to InSideOut Coaching

ISBN 978-1-938254-06-2

Cross Training Publishing
15418 Weir Street #177
Omaha, NE 68137
(308) 293-3891
www.crosstrainingpublishing.com

A MESSAGE FROM
JOE and PAULA

InSideOut Coaching: How Sports Transform Lives, Joe and I hoped to communicate a vision of *InSideOut Coaching*, rooted in empathy and understanding, that we embraced through our own personal and discipleship experiences, and articulated via our coherent narratives. Together for more than 37 years, Joe and I continue to develop individual narratives, as well as a collective coherent narrative that continues to unfold, in new ways every day. It is through learning how to process and integrate all of our experiences that has helped to keep us open, humble, empathic, and free to be the vessels that, along with grace, demonstrate the presence of virtuous and godly character we hope to model.

We invite our readers to co-journey with us as we share together our life narratives and the common hurts, histories, and hopes of all coaches, leaders, and adults with power and authority in the lives of young people.

We are delighted to be partnering with Mark Hull, our teammates on the FCA Wisconsin Staff, and the Fellowship of Christian Athletes team across the country! We are deeply grateful for the hard work, team spirit, and tenacity dedicated to the completion of this project.

Joe and I understand the gospel today, because yesterday, we were invited to come into community, just as we were. There were no walls to this community. There was no uniform to wear. And even once we were there, we weren't told WHAT to think. We were challenged to think for ourselves, and encouraged to become all that we were created to be!

It was a community where we were free to be; free to be cared for; free to learn; free to speak; free to hear; free to explore new possibilities. No one slammed the door to the Kingdom in our faces. No one said we had to change before we could enter. The door was wide open and joyfulness was apparent along with freedom.

When Joe and I think of the overall spirit of discipleship related to and our personal, transformational experience with a Christian community, our prayer is that this same spirit of openness and acceptance; a 'come as you are' tone, penetrates the sense of community through your love for one another. Act confidently, as God gives us everything we need to make this journey home and to finish the race well!

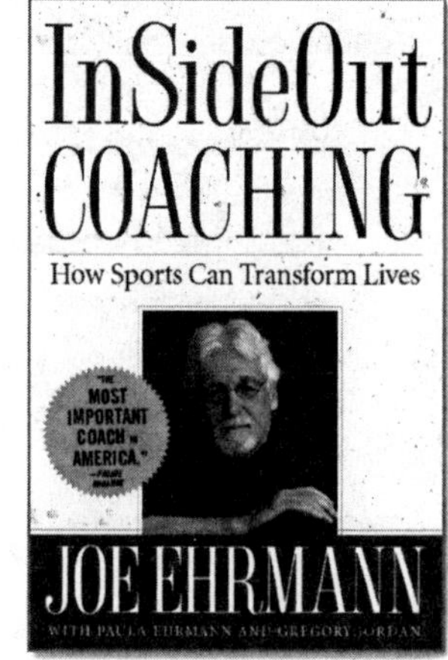

We dedicate this study to our brothers and sisters at Search Ministries, who loved us, taught us well, and released us to develop our unique gifts to help build God's Kingdom. We love you.

In God's Grace,
Paula and Joe Ehrmann

The Fellowship of Christian Athletes and Coach for America congratulate you on your willingness to enter a transformational journey of contemplation and self-assessment. We are very excited about partnering with you on this journey. While it is work that requires great courage and humility, the end product reaps great joy and rewards. We want to offer our help, support and encouragement each step of the way.

"Do not conform any longer to the pattern of this world but be transformed by the renewing of your mind." Romans 12:2

As coaches, we often feel a great deal of pressure to compete according to worldly standards of wins and losses and Xs and Os. This pressure often leads us to conform to a transactional style of coaching based on performance and reward. We believe God calls us to a higher standard of coaching. Transformational coaching results in making an impact in the lives of others that lives on long after we're gone. Transformational Coaching occurs when we first allow God to transform us.

God gives us His Word, His Spirit, and His people to guide us in becoming all that we can be. The coaching principles for godly, effective, life-changing impact are abundant in the Bible. Using the Bible in conjunction with Joe Ehrmann's book, *InSideOut Coaching* (ISO Coaching), we have designed a series of weekly studies constructed as lampposts along the often lonely, bumpy and pressure filled road of coaching.

We believe that God has called us to a higher ground in sports. In order to be agents of change and to challenge status quo standards of character and competition, we must be transformed. Through our transformation, God then empowers us to transform others. This transformational coaching style requires the renewing of our minds on a daily basis.

We believe that God has called us to prepare and equip you on this exciting and challenging adventure on which you are about to embark. We trust that God will give you all that's necessary to be successful.

FCA's Coaches Ministry Purpose
To redeem* sports through the transformed coach

CFA's Purpose Statement
To use sports and coaching to build God's Kingdom

*To restore to its original purpose in the Kingdom.

TABLE OF CONTENTS

Winning While Living a Legacy

InSideOut COACHING Seminar

COMING SOON

CoachForAmerica.com

- DVD's plus Workbook
- Copy of InSideOut Coaching
- 12 Week Coaches Curriculum and Daily Lesson Plans
- Special Bonus: Laminated Coaches Code of Conduct

Jesus was a coach and understands transformational coaching. He knows what you're up against. He watches the pressures and demands of fans wanting to be entertained. He has compassion for your frustration with parents who seem only concerned with what is best for their children, rather than for all the children on the team. He's experienced wins and triumphs as well as disagreements and betrayals on His own team. He understands how the crowd can love and support you one moment and turn against you the next. Using the ISO transformative principles for coaching, we will be rebuilding your house on a solid foundation that will be able to withstand the winds and the rains that inevitably arise during the course of coaching.

The study is 12 sessions long and highlights transformational coaching principles as they correspond to the chapters in ISO Coaching. Each lesson should take 30-60 minutes of preparation time.** Each session is designed to last 60 minutes in a group setting.

For this study you will need:

- *InSideOut Coaching: How Sports Can Transform Lives*
- Notebook
- Bible
- Study Guide

**This study is not a replacement for the ISO Coaching seminar™ and will not cover the same material. The seminar is strongly recommended as foundational and offers practical support for the principles we'll be learning.

You and the other coaches in your group are about to begin what could be the most significant training you will ever have as a coach. This study will help you use the power, privilege and position of "coach" as an agent of transformation in the lives of the athletes entrusted to you. As a result of this study you will have greater clarity on how God's Kingdom, His will and rule that we pray for, could actually become real in the sports world.

"Therefore everyone who hears these words of mine and puts them into practice is like a wise person who built his house on the rock, the rain came down, the streams rose and the winds blew and beat against that house, yet it did not fall because it had its foundation on the rock." – Matthew 7:24

HOW TO GET THE MOST FROM THIS STUDY

Listed below are the segments of each study as well as some hints for getting the most out of this journey.

PREGAME

Each week you will have a chapter to read from *InSideOut Coaching* as well as assigned Bible passages. You will find listed some themes to look for and keep in mind as you read.

GAME PLAN

Here you will find a brief description of the overarching focus, goals and objectives of the session.

WARM UP

A question or two related to the session will be listed for you to draw from your personal experience and share.

GAME TIME

Several questions will be listed for your response related directly to the integration of chapter content and Bible passages. You will find steps that take you through the process that results in the Transformational Principle the session addresses. Writing the answers to these questions will help you and others in your group get the most out of your time together.

POST GAME

Just as after each contest you as a coach look to address what is needed to prepare for the next, so too, we do the same. You are asked, in light of the Game Time participation, what you need to do as a result.

TRANSFORMATIONAL PRINCIPLE

The transformative principle drawn from the session is positively stated in a single sentence.

MEMORY VERSE

The Bible tells us that the way to keep from being conformed by the pressures of the sports world is through the renewing of our minds. One of the best ways to renew our minds is to commit scripture to memory. At the end of each study is a memory verse related to the content of the session.

THE InSideOut PROCESS

"The most competing and durable glory of coaching is to use the whistle for its transformative and not its authoritative power."
Pages 7-8

PREGAME:

InSideOut Coaching Reading:

Introduction: pages 3-10

Themes to keep in mind: Honest reflection and evaluation of the various influences in your life that have formed your current coaching behaviors and attitudes. The wake-up call.

Bible Readings:

Romans 12:1-2

Matthew 23:25-28

Themes to keep in mind: conformity, hypocrisy, honesty, courage, transformation, renewal, worship.

GAME PLAN:

In this chapter, Joe describes coming to a critical impasse in his life. This begins a journey that leads him to the understanding that without transforming himself from the inside out, he will always have problems conforming to old patterns and defaulting to externally imposed standards. True transformation comes from a commitment to the renewing of our minds through spiritual disciplines, living in community, and serving others. This study introduces the InSideOut process and the simple, yet profound and imperative call to us as coaches, to offer all of our coaching goals, attitudes and behaviors up to God as an act of worship.

WARM UP:

What are the factors that led to you committing to a weekly study of InSideOut Coaching?

GAME TIME:

On page 7 of ISO Coaching, Joe describes connecting to old memories as a way of understanding his violent behavior in sports. What is the specific connection that Joe makes here and what is its relevance to the InSideOut process?

Transformational Coaching requires that you dig deep to find the core of your beliefs and emotional reactions. On page 8, Joe states that, "How we make sense of our lives dictates how we live them."

What does Joe mean by this statement?

Can you recall a time when someone coached, taught, or parented you in a way that caused you fear? Explain.

Have you ever coached, taught, or parented someone in a similar fashion? Explain.

Have you ever been surprised, frightened, or disappointed by a behavior in your coaching career that seemed out of character for you? Explain.

As you consider this, how does it make you feel at this moment? (pick two)

Excited	Hopeful	Fearful	Anxious	Defensive
Sad	Confused	Shameful	Empathic	Intimidated

Explain:

Read Matthew 23:25-28

Jesus directed some of His harshest words to people (especially those in places of influence) who acted one way in public for show, but were actually quite different in their hearts.

Why do you think Jesus was so passionate about this?

Living a legacy as a coach requires integrity first. If we do not know ourselves, we are susceptible to the same subtle forces of hypocrisy that divided the minds of the Pharisees.

Take a moment and reflect on your current coaching experiences. Think of a particular aspect of your coaching that you might demonstrate as an act of worship in front of Jesus.

Read Romans 12:1-2

Paul tells us in this passage that we are transformed by the renewing of our minds. This renewing takes commitment to the spiritual disciplines. In ISO Coaching, we learn that past experiences and external forces can control us if we are not purposeful in the renewal of our minds. Becoming an InSideOut Coach requires willingness to courageously "take on" this process of renewing, unflinchingly and without hesitation.

Write Romans 12:1-2 as a personal commitment: in 1st person, adding your name (ex. I, Coach Smith, in view of God's mercy, offer my body as a living sacrifice, holy and pleasing to God...)

POST GAME:

The journey to becoming an ISO Coach can be exciting but also overwhelming as you begin to reflect on the process of renewing your whole mind.

How often do you honestly reflect on and evaluate your life?

With whom are you totally honest?

Renewing our minds requires honest reflection of ourselves.
What is most intimidating to you about this?

What is most exciting to you about this?

TRANSFORMATIONAL PRINCIPLE:

ISO Coaching begins with an intentional process of understanding yourself so that you can renew your mind, be transformed, and impact the athletes you coach for life.

MEMORY VERSE:

I,____, do not conform to the patterns of this world but am transformed by the renewing of my mind, offering up my coaching as a spiritual act of worship.
(Romans 12:2 in 1st person)

"To be empathic, to be instructive, and to have an impact as coaches, we have to find our own narrative first...if you want to be a better coach, you have to be a better you."
Page 43

PREGAME:

InSideOut Coaching Reading:

Chapter One: pages 11-44

Themes to keep in mind: transactional vs. transformational relationships, honesty with self, the power of unprocessed past, the impact and responsibility of coaches.

Bible Readings:

Romans 8:5-17

Luke 6:37-41, 43-46

John 11:38-44

Themes to keep in mind: blind hypocrisy vs. spirit controlled coaching, openness to our flawed nature and the need for redemption.

GAME PLAN:

This first chapter of InSideOut Coaching is a sports biography that Joe writes to illustrate how his earlier developmental experiences affected him. He writes explicitly, at times, about the distorted beliefs and painful emotions that he carried from these memories into every aspect of his life. Scripture is clear on the insidious power of that which remains in the dark and equally clear on the redemptive power of God to bring light into that same place. In this week's study, we are challenged to begin the arduous task of honestly looking at our own stories. When we do this with an open heart, we begin to see who and what is really in charge of us and challenged to remove the grave clothes that bind us. Your first step as an ISO/ Transformational Coach boils down to the profound realization that if you want God to use you to transform others, you might want to consider letting God transform you first!

WARM UP:

We all have memorable sports moments, positive and negative. Share one of your most memorable sports moments from childhood:

GAME TIME:

Joe writes about the "game changers" in his life. These were profound moments and/or experiences that shifted him into a particular direction.

Can you think of a couple of "game changers" in your life that have shifted your direction? Explain.

Why do you think Joe bothers to tell his story? What is the significance of his reference to himself as a "wounded healer" on page 13?

Read Romans 8:5-17

What do you think coaching by sinful nature vs. coaching by Spirit might look like?

Discuss an experience when have you been your BEST as a Coach?

Discuss an experience when you have been your WORST as a Coach?

Read Luke 6:37-41

In the introduction chapter, we looked at Jesus' condemnation of hypocrisy. In these verses, we are reminded again of the seriousness of judging others and particularly of spiritual arrogance, when we are still blind to what is disjointed inside of us.

What do you find most interesting, intimidating, exciting, or overwhelming about Jesus' strong challenge to leaders?

Read Luke 6:46

Is your coaching integrated or dis-integrated with the rest of your life (i.e. your faith, values, beliefs, etc.)? Give examples.

On page 43, Joe says, "Every coach has a story…to be empathic, to be instructive, and to have an impact as coaches, we have to find our own narrative first – understand them, contain and bind them. If you want to be a better coach, you have to become a better you."

Jesus would agree with Joe.

Read Luke 3:43-45

How is your heart revealed in your coaching behavior?

Read John 11:38-44

What old memories keep you from being fully alive to life and to your players?

POST GAME:

What are the next steps you will take this week to move toward a more integrated, Spirit-filled, transformational approach to your coaching?

Journaling:

Reflection:

Sports Biography:

Asking for Feedback:

Spiritual Disciplines:

Other:

TRANSFORMATIONAL PRINCIPLE:

InSideOut Coaching begins with a commitment to the process of knowing yourself.

MEMORY VERSE:

"For God, who said, 'Let light shine out of darkness,' made his light shine in our hearts to give us the light of the knowledge of the glory of God in the face of Christ."
2 Corinthians 4:6

"Playing for Coach Simmons required a consuming devotion to rejoice and be glad."
Page 51

PREGAME:

InSideOut Coaching Reading:

Chapter 2: pages 45-67

Themes to keep in mind: the power of coach memories, modeling the best, the journey to self-discovery.

Bible Readings:

Psalm 139:14-16

John 15:12-17

John 13:12-17

Themes to keep in mind: God's creativity, individual uniqueness, leadership styles, servanthood.

GAME PLAN:

Coaches have a long, lasting impact on the players they coach. On page 50 of ISO Coaching, Joe reminds us that, "Great coaching demands introspection, integrity, and integration of the coach's life history." Transformational Coaches have the freedom to be whoever God created them to be. In Chapter 1, we looked at the importance of confronting the vices that limit us in order to free up the virtues that become God's wings upon which we can fly. God wants to use you – wherever you are – with your unique personality and even your brokenness – wherever you are. God will find your diamond in the rough and show you how to use it mightily right where you are.

WARM UP:

When it comes to the 1st level of coaching (tactics & techniques), who has been your greatest influence? What made this coach a good teacher?

GAME TIME:

When it comes to the 2nd (mind) & 3rd (heart & spirit) levels of coaching, who are the coaches, teachers, parents who have impacted your style and philosophy of coaching?

Write down 3 positive aspects you have modeled after influential coaches.

Level One (tactics & techniques):

Level Two (mind):

Level Three (heart & spirit):

Joe points to 3 personal coaching role models who have influenced his coaching behaviors, attitudes and philosophies. Each of these individuals is very different in their "coaching styles."

What did Joe see in each of these Coaching Models that he desired to emulate:

Coach Simmons (pages 50-57):

Dorothy (pages 57-64):

Moses (pages 64-67):

Read Psalm 139:14-16

What strikes you most about this verse?

Have you considered that God does not make mistakes and has not made ANY mistakes in creating YOU?

Take a moment to consider how YOU in your uniqueness are part of the plan to carry out the Holy Will of God. In considering God's hand in making you uniquely you, what virtues do you want to define your coaching?

Jesus was a gifted teacher, mentor and the ultimate coach! His methods were non-traditional and often strikingly in defiance of the status quo. Jesus stood in truth, despite the world telling him to do it their way.

Identify Jesus' unique coaching techniques in the following passages:

Read John 15:12-17

Lesson:

Coaching Technique:

Read John 13:12-17

Lesson:

Coaching Technique:

Reread pages 50-51 of ISO Coaching:

In this section of the book, Joe describes Coach Simmons' SIMPLE yet, profound locker room speech that has defined his love of God, others and the sport. If we are not living out of our passion, then our vices are likely to get the best of us.

What are some beliefs, behaviors and destructive factors that cause you, at times, to lose your love for others and your love of the game?

Is your coaching MARKED by your love for YOUR PLAYERS and the game?

Following Jesus demands a consuming devotion to rejoice and be glad! What consuming devotion does it take to play for me? To what am I asking my players to be devoted?

POST GAME:

Write a commitment statement below, describing how you intend to become a Coaching Role Model for your players:

I, Coach _________________, commit to the following vision:

Signed: ____ Date: ____________________

TRANSFORMATIONAL PRINCIPLE

ISO coaches confront their vices, nurture their virtues and become heroes in the lives of those they coach.

MEMORY VERSE:

"Love is patient, love is kind. It does not envy, it does not boast, it is not proud. It is not rude, it is not self-seeking, it is not easily angered, it keeps no record of wrongs. Love does not delight in evil but rejoices with the truth. It always protects, always trusts, always hopes, always perseveres. Love never fails."

I Corinthians 13:4-8a

Notes:

A COMPLEX TRANSACTION

"The two most powerful words in the English language are 'coach says...', but great power requires great character for that coach's words to be a blessing and not a curse."
Mark Hull

PREGAME:

InSideOut Coaching Reading:

Chapter 3: pages 68-88

Themes to keep in mind: basic developmental needs of youth, triggers & logs, virtuous vs. destructive/transactional vs. transformational coaching.

Bible Readings:

Exodus 34:5-7

Romans 7: 14-25

Numbers 20: 7-12

Matthew 11:28-30

Themes to keep in mind: consequences of unchecked behavior, generational sin, transformational vs. transactional spirituality.

GAME PLAN:

Overwhelmed by the response elicited from the *Parade Magazine* article, Joe and Paula began recognizing dysfunctional coaching patterns in the thousands of stories. We will review the needs of our youth identified in the "Hardwired to Connect" study and look to the power of coach to coach according to the needs of the player, rather than those of the coach. In this week's study, we will take a look at the destructive realities of transactional coaching as well as the exciting and virtuous possibilities of transformational coaching, as modeled through our Head Coach, Jesus.

WARM UP:

Was there ever a time when you felt coached, based solely on your performance? How did it feel when you didn't perform for this coach? How did this coach demonstrate transactional behavior?

GAME TIME:

Early on, we are introduced to the concept of coach as mentor, "a title conveying an undeniable obligation to care for a player's welfare, instruct them in virtue, and guide them toward an adulthood of citizenship and contemplation." The Hardwired to Connect study introduced on page 73 lists 3 basic needs of every young person.

Write a short description of those needs:

1) Belong

2) Belief

3) Base Community

Read pages 74-86

What is your initial reaction to reading these descriptions?

With which of these transactional coaching styles have you had experience?

Dictators?

Bullies:

Narcissists:

Saints:

Misfits:

Read Exodus 34:5-7

How does “sin” or “dysfunctional behavior” get passed down from generation to generation?

Have you witnessed this in your life or the lives of others you care about?

If this pattern can occur in a family, is it possible for "sin" or "dysfunctional behavior" to occur on a team? Explain.

Read Romans 7:14-25

In these verses, Paul writes about how difficult discernment can be because we are bound up in the struggles against our own self-deceit. We discussed Jesus' warning in Luke 6 to leaders regarding the hypocrisy in judging others when we should be looking at ourselves. Paul presents the gospel of grace here, clearly from the integrity of his heart.

What is the unique technique that Paul demonstrates here in his presentation of the gospel?

Would you call Paul a Transformational or Transactional Coach? Why?

On page 86, Joe introduces the concept of triggers and shares a painful example from his own life. We all have triggers. Some are bigger than others. Some, we are aware of, and some remain just beneath the surface. Some explode on the outside and some explode on the inside.

Read Numbers 20:7-12

What was Moses' trigger?

How aware are you of all your triggers?

Circle the potential triggers in your life:

losing a game	angry people	"lazy" people
arrogant people	being stuck in traffic	being left out
being ridiculed	feeling betrayed	jealousy
being tired	being hungry	being questioned
transitions	other: ______________________	

Read Matthew 11: 28-30

Jesus and Paul share a remarkable humility in the invitation they present to the world. Because he deeply understood his own wretchedness, Paul understands the beauty of the gospel. He understands the words of his own Transformational Mentor, Jesus, who offered him rest for his weary soul.

Why do you think humility is a critical virtue of the Transformational Coach?

Do you consider yourself a humble person? Why or Why not?

POST GAME:

Write down 3 transactional coaching behaviors that you are going to work on improving during these next 10 weeks:

Write down 3 action steps that you are going to take to ensure that you are meeting the 3 basic needs of your players:

TRANSFORMATIONAL PRINCIPLE:

InSideOut Coaches transform others through the humble demonstration of their own personal transformation.

MEMORY VERSE:

"Whatever happens, conduct yourselves in a manner worthy of the gospel of Christ."

Philippians 1:27

"Progress has many overpriced ideas, but trading in play for organized competition is one of its most uncharitable."
Mark Hull

PREGAME:

InSideOut Coaching Reading

Chapter 4: pages 89-106

Themes to keep in mind while reading: The importance of play, the cultural lies of femininity and masculinity, the absence of play in sports, the role of coaches in protecting and encouraging the safety and innocence of our youth.

Bible Readings

Matthew 18:1-6, Mark 10:13-16

1 Corinthians 9:24-27; 13:4-8

Genesis 1:26-28

Themes to keep in mind while reading: True masculinity and femininity, the spiritual innocence of children, the role of innocence in faith, the spiritual responsibility of coaches, the playful heart of God.

GAME PLAN:

In this chapter, Joe writes about the distortion of play in the game of sports. He outlines social and cultural factors that contribute to the loss of childhood innocence and to the reinforcement of transactional relationship styles. Jesus reminds us in scripture that it is this very innocence that is required to enter the kingdom of heaven and yet, the world is anxious to steal this innocence from our children and from us. This study looks at the factors influencing the 'play' in the game and encourages coaches to connect with their own loss of innocence and to develop an effective plan for bringing the safety of play back onto the field for the sake of their athletes' souls.

WARM UP:

When it comes to games (not the sport you coach), which word better characterizes your participation: Play or Compete? Explain.

GAME TIME:

On page 89 of ISOC, Joe writes about the pure joy and delight of tobogganing all day long as a boy on a snowy hill in Buffalo. He goes on to say that he has seldom felt that same "great sensation" in organized sports. He states on page 89 that children go from, "...the unbridled joy of creative play to the performance based world of driven parents and overly competitive coaches."

Joe states that "playing" in organized sports has become almost impossible for our children. Why or why not?

Joe discusses 3 cultural lies of masculinity and femininity that disrupt our natural development, rob us of our innocence, and give us a false sense of identity.

Define how each of these lies has impacted your development and could be impacting your current self-image. (Beliefs, Buying habits, Language, Ethics, etc.)

Lies of Masculinity – Ball Field, Bedroom, and Billfold

Lies of Femininity – Prince Charming Myth, Beauty & Body Type, and Abandonment of Self

How do you see these cultural lies at work in the lives of your athletes? (Locker room talk, music, dress, promiscuity, sense of inadequacy, etc.)

Read Genesis 1:26-28

In vs. 26, we read: "Then God said, 'Let US make human beings in OUR image, in OUR likeness...and let them rule over the earth..." and in vs. 27, "so God created human beings in his own image, in the image of God he created them; male and female he created them."

Using only these verses, redefine masculinity and femininity and what it means to be created in the image of God:

Relational: (God lives in community)

Purposeful: (God is intentional)

Masculinity & Femininity = Relational & Purposeful

Rewrite in your own words what it means to be a man or a woman created in the image of God, according to Genesis 1:26-28.

In Matthew 18:1-6 and Mark 10:13-16, Jesus tells His disciples that, "...unless they become like little children, they will never enter the kingdom of God..." What do you think Jesus meant when He said this?

Why do we frequently call ourselves "children of God" and what is the significance of this terminology?

Consider how you might maintain the 'innocence' of your faith in a culture that is constantly trying to take it away. How difficult might this be for your athletes? Explain:

In 1 Corinthians 9:24-27, what is the everlasting "Crown" we are competing for to which Paul refers?

How does the pursuit of this crown relate to the protection of the faith and innocence of our athletes?

Jesus calls us to be light in a dark world. Joe has challenged us to question the tenants of our transactional style of coaching and to become Ambassadors of Play (to protect the play of the game for the sake of the innocence of the athlete – the trust, faith, safety, boundaries and consistency that a Transformational Coach who is emotionally healthy and grounded in her/his faith provides) who cares more about the person than about his/her performance.

POSTGAME:

What are three ways in which you can counter the lies of masculinity/femininity in your own life?

In the lives of your athletes?

What can you do to keep play from being pushed out of your coaching and out of the circle of sport?

What are 3 specific action steps you can take, as an ISO-Coach, to help keep your athletes focused on winning the Everlasting Crown referred to in 1 Cor. 9: 24-25?

TRANSFORMATIONAL PRINCIPLE:

InSideOut Coaches provide safe environments and opportunities for young people to play, grow, experience and interpret life.

MEMORY VERSE:

"This is the day that the Lord has made; Let us rejoice and be glad in it."
Psalm 118:24

Notes:

"Would you tell me, please, which way I ought to go from here?"
"That depends a good deal on where you want to get to," said the Cat.
"I don't much care where –," said Alice
"Then is doesn't matter which way you go," said the Cat.
"– so long as I get SOMEWHERE," Alice added...
Alice's Adventures in Wonderland, Lewis Carroll

PREGAME:

InSideOut Coaching Reading:

Chapter 5: pages 107-125

Themes to keep in mind: Social contract, self examination, self understanding, goal setting, purposeful coaching.

Bible Readings:

Colossians 1:9-13

Luke 4:1-13

Galatians 5:19-24

Themes to keep in mind: the Spirit's presence and power in us, our inheritance, how to battle temptations, human results vs. Spiritual fruit.

GAME PLAN:

In the first four chapters, we have traveled with Joe as he mindfully constructs his coherent life narrative. In this final chapter of the first half of the book, Joe challenges us to continue the heavy internal lifting in preparation for the external manifestation of our transformed hearts. We have learned the importance of understanding our stories and making sense of our past experiences. We have reviewed the toxic nature of transactional coaching and unchecked triggered responses. We should have a sense by now that this process of understanding and disciplining what is within us is an arduous and ongoing task, one that we cannot do without God.

Chapter 5 requires that you set aside significant time to process through your answers to the FOUR CRITICAL COACHING QUESTIONS. Even though you will come back to this chapter and these questions several times for refinement, the unique answers you develop, along with God's guidance, will be the compass and roadmap you need for the rest of your coaching life as an ISO Coach.

WARMUP:

Joe talks about the importance of a Sports Social Contract that would focus on the rights and welfare of children and the responsibilities of adults to provide for and protect those rights.

In order to protect our youth, what is the one thing that you would change about sports in America, to better support the developmental needs of youth that we discussed back in Chapter 4, The Play's The Thing?

GAME TIME:

Why do I coach?

Without a purpose statement, I am like Alice just walking around in the woods waiting to get "somewhere."

On page 109, Joe states that answering this question can, "...help coaches identify selfish agendas and develop a purpose that transcends personal, vocational, financial, or ego-driven needs."

Write Joe's "Why" statement from page 110:

Read Colossians 1:9-13

What is the purpose we all share as children of God?

How do Paul and Timothy portray their purpose statement in this letter of encouragement to their teammates in Colossi?

Why do I coach the way I do?

Without understanding my story, I am blinded to my own strengths, weaknesses, philosophies, triggers and behaviors.

Joe developed his coherent narrative to make sense of his coaching behaviors, attitudes and patterns. This required time, patience, lots of prayer and a willingness to look at some things that were painful and difficult.

Read Luke 4:1-13

Why do you think the Jesus, the Son of God, full of the Holy Spirit, chose to spend forty difficult days in the desert?

How can we gain strength through the identification and testing of our weaknesses?

What does it feel like to be coached by me?

Without purposeful coaching and mindful awareness, my players fall prey to my defaulted transactional style.

On page 120, Joe discusses the core values that are essential to his character, constitution and coaching. Joe's core values are empathy, kindness & service to others.

Read Galatians 5:19-24

How does Paul illustrate through these verses the process of our core values leaking from the inside out to others?

In reading vs. 22, what "fruit" do you seem to struggle producing?

How do I measure success?

Without redefining success, I will measure it according to the win/loss standards of the world versus the measurement of my purpose statement.

Write John Wooden's definition of success. (pages 123-124)

How has this definition defined his character as well as his coaching career?

How might Jesus define success in coaching?

POST GAME:

We've been in training for five weeks now. You have spent numerous hours reflecting on the formation of your life in and out of sports. It's time to fashion what you've learned on this inward journey into a focused written purpose statement. If you don't have a "Why" statement to share with parents and other coaches it's time to start drafting one. Don't worry – it's a work in progress! Share your purpose with the group.

I, Coach ____________________________________, coach to

Write out your Purpose Statement on a 3 x 5 card and carry it with you this week. Tweak it until it fits like a glove!

Challenger Action Step: ask your players what it feels like to be coached by you.

TRANSFORMATIONAL PRINCIPLE:

InSideOut Coaches are clear, purposeful, directed and driven by compassion because they understand who they are and to what they have been called.

MEMORY VERSE:

"Finally, brothers and sisters, whatever is true, whatever is noble, whatever is right, whatever is pure, whatever is lovely, whatever is admirable – if anything is excellent or praiseworthy – think about such things. Whatever you have learned or received or heard from me, or seen in me – put it into practice. And the God of peace will be with you."

Philippians 4:8-9

Notes:

"We are caught in an inescapable network of mutuality, tied in a single garment of destiny. Whatever affects one directly, affects all indirectly."
Dr. Martin Luther King, Jr.

PREGAME:

InSideOut Coaching Reading:

Chapter 6: pages 134-156

Themes to keep in mind: the importance of community, building and maintaining community, identifying and tearing down walls that divide and destroy community, essential virtues to fostering community.

Bible Readings:

Ephesians 4:11-16

Galatians 3:28

Matthew 22:34-40

Themes to keep in mind: The distribution of gifts, the spirituality of oneness in Christ, the greatest of commandments, love as a noun vs. love as a verb, non-optional authentic community.

GAME PLAN:

During the first six sessions of study, we looked at the process of going inside and began the work of understanding ourselves, our past, our motivations, philosophies, experiences and even our emotional and behavioral triggers. In understanding the cultural complexities and developmental needs of our players, you, hopefully by now, have begun to formulate a clearer, more precise purpose statement that is custom designed according to your gifts and God's calling in your life.

The primary thesis of the first five chapters of ISO Coaching is the profound understanding that change begins on the inside. At CFA and FCA, we strongly believe that Transformational Coaching results when coaches first take care of their own house – the house in which their own soul abides.

In Chapter Six we begin to turn the corner from the InSideOut. This chapter starts the process of taking the inside work of chapters 1-5 to the field! We will look at the first of the five pillars through which the transformational experience takes place – Community. We need each other. We belong to each other. We are called to serve one another. Biblically, we can find no greater call than to the responsibility and privilege of true community. It is no coincidence that Joe starts here, as authentic community is the pillar through which the others find their strength. Chapter Six also kicks off the discussion of Virtue as the pillar of Transformational Coaching.

WARM UP:

Authentic community is based on the inherent value and worth of every person in that community.

What's the most authentic community experience you've had through sports? Explain what made this experience "authentic."

GAME TIME:

On pages 137-138, Joe discusses the concepts of team and community. He uses these terms interchangeably in these passages.

Describe in your own words, how "team" is a synonym for "community":

Read Ephesians 4:11-13

What do these verses tell us about the distribution of gifts on God's team?

On page 136, Joe writes about creating a team without walls, yet one with a solid foundation.

Take a minute to write down and examine the three solid foundation principles of a team without walls:

1.

2.

3.

ISO Coaching establishes three foundational virtues that form the core of this type of team/community:

Pages 141-143 - Liberty: Liberty gives people the permission to embrace who they really are and the power to do what is good and right. The intent of every rule is to provide and/or protect so that we can function freely. Biff and Joe believe that liberty and community are inseparable and that every great team must recognize three basic realities:

1. We ______________________________________ to each other: Full acceptance and servant leadership.
2. We ______________________________________ to each other: Inhibited by both feelings of inferiority and superiority.
3. We ______________________________________ each other: We don't give our all to the game; we give our all to the team.

Without liberty, there are factions. Where there are factions, there are problems with community. When authentic community is taught, but factions are experienced, the pillar begins to crack.

Read Galatians 3:28

Can you remember a time when you felt excluded from the

team/community/others?

Where do factions show up on your team?

How might you address these factions preemptively?

Jesus is a liberator! "He who the Son sets free is truly free!" Living in restrictive and fearful ways at times, we forget that Jesus offers us an opportunity to experience more liberty, more freedom and more unique self-expression than we could ever imagine.

How free, how 'at liberty' do you feel as a coach? Where have you felt the pull of your core beliefs in one direction and the pull of the culture and the past in another?

Who do you talk to about these struggles?

On pages 144-151, Joe discusses respect and why this virtue is fundamental to authentic community along with Liberty and Moral Courage.

Read Matthew 22:34-40

When Jesus was asked by the 'religious experts' of His day, which was the greatest of the commandments, He didn't hesitate to answer that it was to Love

God COMPLETELY and to love others AS OURSELVES. This presupposes a couple of things. That we first and foremost love God, and second, that we cannot love our neighbors intentionally UNLESS we have learned how to love OURSELVES appropriately.

What does this say about the importance of dealing with issues like self-respect, low self-esteem, envy, false pride, etc.?

Respect begins inwardly. In sharing his own personal journey, Joe states that peace with ourselves and our own stories leads to respect and empathy for others and their stories. Respect fosters healthy relationships. Joe and Biff's mantra "Just Love 'em" helps to keep focus in an environment where sarcasm, condemnation and shaming have no place.

How often in sports have you heard the phrase, "I was disrespected!" What was usually the result of incidents when this became the interpretation?

Joe writes about a "no-cut" policy on their team. Acknowledging that there are some sports situations where this is not possible, how can you respectfully handle cutting a player from a team if you have to?

How can this same "respectful" attitude and approach be extended to officials, other teams, and coaches?

On pages 151-157, Joe adds the virtue of moral courage to liberty and respect. This third leg in the tripod of community helps support the virtues of liberty and respect. Moral courage is required in doing what you believe is right in the face of opposition, criticism, ridicule or any other personal cost. A Transformational Coach is provided with numerous opportunities to model moral courage with the intent of training his/her players in how to think through and make moral choices.

Do you find yourself spending more time upholding and validating physical courage or moral courage among your players?

Share an act of moral courage you've personally witnesses connected to sports:

"Teaching moral courage as a coach requires Moral Courage of a coach."

Where do you see opportunities as a coach to demonstrate moral courage? (Locker room, lunch room, game, practice, after a loss)

How can you affirm acts of Moral Courage by your players?

POST GAME:

Write three action steps that you are going to take to create authentic community in your team where everyone is needed, valued and ascribed worth:

Yourself:

Your Players:

Your Captains:

Other Coaches:

Parents:

Are you currently in authentic Christian community?

Is your coaching staff?

If not, what action step will you take to experience God's will for your life in this area?

TRANSFORMATIONAL PRINCIPLE:

InSideOut Coaches create a community based on the inherent value and worth of each and every player; a community supported by mutual respect and protected by moral courage.

MEMORY VERSE:

"Love the Lord your God with all your heart and with all your soul and with all your mind and with all your strength.

The second is this:
'Love your neighbor as yourself.'
There is no commandment greater than these."

Mark 12:30-31

"Imagine the transformation of fields and courts and pools and gyms into classrooms; into authentic, co-curricular experiences that build on the school experience and focus on instruction in virtue! Imagine what would happen to a nation if coaches taught young athletes the true essence of being women and men! Imagine if athletes learned that justice and reason were more critical to their success as human beings than winning and losing."

Page 181, InSideOut Coaching

PREGAME:

InSideOut Coaching Reading:

Chapter 7: pages 157-181

Themes to keep in mind: Sports as a co-curricular, educational vehicle; Integration of classroom model with on-field and off-field activity. The identification and integration of values and virtues delivered through core principles. Coach as Teacher-Coach – more than x's and o's. The identification, development and delivery of a classroom curriculum mindset that will help accomplish your transformative goals.

Bible Readings:

Matthew 7:24-27

James 3:13-18

1 Timothy 4:7-11

1 Peter 1:3-9

Themes to keep in mind: The value of learning about righteousness vs. living in ignorance. Solidifying the foundation and deepening the roots of our faith in preparation for the inevitable challenges of life. Training, building and strengthening the soul. The more profound lessons are the ones taught and caught on the sidelines.

GAME PLAN:

Transformational coaching is built on a clear and compelling purpose statement (WHY) and then taught, nurtured and integrated into every aspect of your coaching. Transformational coaches are teacher-coaches who intentionally use their coaching platform to deliver life-lessons that reinforce their WHY. Lesson plans should be identified and developed out of your own life story (coherent narrative), defined, integrated into coaching and celebrated when displayed. This study examines the thinking and actions involved in creating and implementing your own "classroom after class." You will be encouraged to start processing your own co-curricular messaging based on your narrative, values and virtues.

WARM UP:

The term "co-curricular" designates sports as an educational activity with the potential to develop the physical, academic, social, emotional, moral and civic competence of every player. This makes practice the last classroom of the day. (Page 159)

Do you agree or disagree with this statement? Why? Why not?

Joe identifies three reasons why we should treat sports and coaching as co-curricular:

1. Sport offers young people the opportunity to learn in a different and more holistic way.
2. Sports are built on stories that bond people's lives together in unique ways.
3. Sports offer an opportunity for connection that can help players embrace new learning and start developing their own coherent narrative.

Share a personal story about a life lesson you learned through sports in one of these three areas:

GAME TIME:

As you read through this chapter what impressed you about this co-curricular approach to coaching?

After reading this chapter did you feel more inspired or overwhelmed? Empowered or unequipped?

Joe and Biff identified 3 Core Virtues (page 162) as foundational to the educational dimension of their classroom coaching.

Right now, if you were to pick 3 Core Virtues, what would they be?

1.

2.

3.

Joe and Biff also developed 11 Core Principles (pages 166-7) that support their transformative purpose statement: to help boys and girls become men and women of empathy and integrity who will lead, be responsible and change the world for good.

As you look at these Principles can you see how each principle supports their WHY?

Which of these 11 support your transformative WHY?

What Principles do you need to create to fulfill your WHY?

Joe and Biff use the athletic classroom to counteract and reframe the negative messages that our culture, especially our sports culture, ingrains in us. Once the messages are identified, they teach, model and integrate these lesson in the locker room, on the field, and in life. Jesus was constantly doing this with His team.

Read the conclusion of Christ's sermon in Matthew 7:24-27.

Why do you think Jesus ends His famous Sermon on the Mount with this parable?

What does Jesus' message tell us about the building and maintenance of your transformative coaching?

Think back to a time when a "storm" hit your coaching or team: false accusations, code violations, injuries, parent problems etc. How did your foundation hold up? How well were you prepared and how well did you prepare your team?

We work hard preparing our players physically, but how hard do we work to prepare them for life?

Read 1 Timothy 4:7-9

What does Timothy tell us about the value of physical training vs. training in godliness?

On pages 175-181, we read about Joe and Biff's core value of Contemplation. Contemplation, silence, solitude, and centeredness are critical to the InSideOut work required of a transformational coach. Page 176. Joe reminds us here of the critical importance of training in the spiritual disciplines.

Read James 3:13-18

Why are spiritual disciplines an essential practice of the InSideOut Coach?

James contrasts transactional wisdom of the world with transformational wisdom born out of spiritual disciplines.

How dependent are you on God's coaching through spiritual disciplines?

Put an "x" on the segment of the line that best represents your inclusion of spiritual disciplines into your coaching life:

Never Seldom Sometimes Always

If you have had any practice with any of these disciplines, please feel free to share with the group what you practice, why you practice it, and what effect the particular discipline has had on you, your players and your team.

Spending time with God refuels your tank. What are the spiritual disciplines that you would like to incorporate into your coaching practice this next season? (Bible study or reading, prayer, fasting, journaling, serving, etc.)

POST GAME:

A co-curricular approach cannot be sustained when we attempt to become "tour guides to a land we've never been to." The journey of a thousand miles begins with one step.

What next step do you intend to make so your coaching is co-curricular and what will be the means to develop curriculum and implement it?

Going back to the core values you wrote down and looking at your "next step" response, what thoughts do you have on how you might share these new ideas with other coaches?

OVERTIME:

Joe and Biff coach in a secular school with players of various faith backgrounds. Due to the Separation of Church and State laws and the mission of their school, they are sensitive to the issue of sharing the Gospel. Instead, Joe and Biff focus on issues of spirituality, contextualizing Bible truths, and utilizing Old Testament teachings on social justice that are inclusive of most faith traditions.

If you coach in a public or secular school – how do you approach this issue?

How does this impact your curriculum development?

Take a few moments to discuss as a group.

TRANSFORMATIONAL PRINCIPLE:

Transformational coaches are teacher-coaches who intentionally use their coaching platform to deliver life-lessons that reinforce their WHY and assist in changing the arc of each and every player's life.

MEMORY VERSE:

"The Lord has told us what is good. What he requires of us is this: to do what is just, to show constant love, and to live in humble fellowship with our God."

Micah 6:8

"Our tongues and our lips are objects of discipline as much as our athletes' muscle memory and training habits."
Page 209

PREGAME:

InSideOut Coaching Reading:

Chapter 8: pages 182-209

Themes to keep in mind: the virtues of clarity and discipline, authenticity, the power of clear communication, codes of conduct.

Bible Readings:

Psalm 77:1-9

2 Corinthians 6:3-10

James 1:19-25

Proverbs 18:21; 19:1-2

3 John 11

Themes to keep in mind: doing before teaching, practicing before preaching, maintaining spiritual connection for all seasons of life.

GAME PLAN:

In this chapter, we begin to get a glimpse at the complexities of InSideOut Coaching. Effectively communicating with our players is not just a matter of sitting down and having a conversation with them. Impactful, life-changing contact and communication can only occur when we are aware of ourselves, connected to God, and able to keep our eyes purposely fixed on the goal of transforming others through the best tool we have, our transformed selves. This chapter looks at some of the challenges we face on this front, and offers some creative and useful tools that help build and reinforce a program that is built on the truth God has given us.

WARM UP:

Think about growing up in your family. Would you characterize your parents as clear and consistent communicators or "read my mind" communicators?

What kind of communicator do you consider yourself?

GAME TIME:

This chapter opens up with a tragic, albeit, not so unusual, example of how we, as coaches, often miss important signals of communication because we are entangled in our own heads and not present for our players. If we are purposeful with a game plan that is not soul-centric, we can easily get distracted and miss the point that we are to love our athletes into Christ.

Read Psalm 77:1-9

The Psalmist is having difficulty, in the midst of a tough time, experiencing the presence of God.

Can you think of a time when you felt alone and perhaps abandoned by God? Explain.

What "signals" would you look for in one of your athletes who might be feeling a similar way?

Read 2 Corinthians 6:3-10

Under what conditions does Paul exempt us from enacting God's love through the power of the Holy Spirit? _________________ (Hint – very short answer)

On pages 186-203, Joe discusses the virtue of Clarity and its role in communication. Clarity as a virtue cannot be achieved when we are not clear about who we are and what we believe. Therefore, clarity requires authenticity. Authenticity requires integrity. As InSideOut/Transformational Coaches, we are learning that our connection to others requires a deep connection to ourselves and to God. Without this deeper, personal connection, we cannot be present for others.

What are the 3 habits that help Transformational Coaches ensure purposeful contact, communication, and connection as described on page 199?

How can you begin to incorporate these habits into your coaching program?

These coaching habits require confidence, assertiveness, warmth, empathy, listening, mentoring and a host of other emotional intelligence skills.

Are you confident engaging in these proactive behaviors?

Was this your personal experience with being coached?

Could you use some coaching yourself in these skills?

Are you willing to ask for support in this area?

On pages 191-197, we see that Biff and Joe developed specific Codes of Conduct for coaches, players and parents in order to communicate expectations CLEARLY.

Write the role of CLARITY in writing these specific Codes of Conduct according to Biff and Joe:

1) for Coaches: (page 190-191)

2) for Parents: (page 193-194)

3) for Players (page 196-197)

Are these Codes of Conduct threatening or empowering to you? Explain.

Read Ephesians 4:22-32; Proverbs 18:21, 19:1-2; 3 John 11

Describe any similarities or differences (if you can) between these verses and the Codes of Conduct we read in ISO Coaching?

On pages 203-4, Joe adds the virtue of discipline and its role in Contact, Communication and Connection. Can you briefly explain how the virtue of discipline is supported in these verses?

Read Ephesians 4:26a – "In your anger, do not sin"

This verse CLARIFIES that anger is not a sin and that we do get angry (created in the image of God, Gen. 1:26-28) just as God gets angry. What we DO with our anger is another story. Just like God, we are created as emotional beings. But with no discipline, we can be just like animals. If we are not aware and in control of our emotions, our emotions can CONTROL, DOMINATE and DESTROY our potential for impact.

Acknowledging and validating emotions is a critical ISO coaching skill. How do you acknowledge and validate your own emotions without sinning?

What tools and rules do you have for Disciplined Communication?

Would you consider using Biff and Joe's VCR or ROARS approach found on pages 206-208?

POST GAME:

Read James 1:19-25

Coach James compares listening to the Word and not doing what it says to looking at ourselves in the mirror and then walking away and forgetting what we look like. It can be tempting to teach the Word without living the Word but when we do, we quickly find ourselves losing clarity.

What is one Action Step you can take to:

CLARIFY your coaching mission statement?

DISCIPLINE your coaching mission statement?

CLARIFY your expectations for yourself as a coach?

DISCIPLINE your expectations for yourself as a coach?

CLARIFY your expectations for your athletes as players?

DISCIPLINE your expectations for your athletes as players?

TRANSFORMATIONAL PRINCIPLE:

InSideOut Coaches are disciplined and clear in the communication and practice of creating effective, life affirming and life-changing environments for players, coaches and their families.

MEMORY VERSE:

"Do not merely listen to the Word, and so deceive yourselves.
DO what it says."
James 1:22

JUST WIN BABY

"Competition, therefore, is not defined by winning or losing, but by the degree to which all competitors realize their fullest potential."
Page 213

PREGAME:

InSideOut Coaching Reading:

Chapter 9: pages 210-232

Themes to keep in mind: definition of competition, socialization and place of winning, role of excellence and empathy in competition.

Bible Readings:

Mark 9:33-36

Matthew 25:14-30

Luke 16:14-15; 23:32-34

Themes to keep in mind: winning in God's kingdom, excellence and empathy defined in scripture.

GAME PLAN:

After spending 10 sessions together building foundational groundwork as InSideOut Coaches, we are ready to approach one of the most difficult and challenging arenas in the sports world – the arena of competition. The meaning and purpose of competition in sports has changed over the centuries, and Transformational Coaches who are working from their purpose statements are steadfast in redefining competition in order to push back against the culturally conformed pressure to "win at all costs." This session's study takes a look at healthy competition; challenges us to confront egocentric driven concepts around winning and losing; and encourage us to approach competition through honoring key virtues of empathy and excellence.

WARM UP:

Joe opens up this chapter with a story about playing against his toughest competition, John Hannah, from the New England Patriots.

How was John Hannah's conduct on the field different from Joe's and how do you think their view of competition differed at the time?

GAME TIME:

"Winning isn't everything, it's the only thing." Despite our efforts to be "good sports," we usually want to win and we usually feel bad when we don't. This is largely due to social conditioning, low esteem, and the fact that beating someone and coming out on top is rewarded while losing is overtly or covertly punished. We tend to give the trophies to the winners while the losers get grief (or at the very least, get called "the losers").

Read Mark 9:33-36

According to Jesus, who "wins"?

On page 213, Joe gives us a NEW definition of Competition. What is it?

Read Matthew 25:14-30 and page 228 of ISO Coaching.

How is excellence defined by this parable?

Name two ways that performance/faithful service/excellence are rewarded.

As Joe notes, the sports world's allegiance to the scoreboard creates a dilemma for the transformational coach. Jesus spoke very directly about competing allegiances while speaking to the religiously powerful and socially connected people of His day. His words speak directly to our sports culture today.

Read Luke 16:14-15 (substituting the word "winning" for "money")

As we "justify ourselves in the eyes of others," what is highly esteemed and valued in the sports culture?

What do you find most challenging about learning and integrating this new definition of competition for yourself?

On page 218, Joe emphasizes AGAIN, the critical importance of EMPATHY in transformational coaching and, in particular, as it relates to winning and losing.

Why does Joe make such a strong connection between empathy and healthy competition?

Think about the last time your team was slaughtered. Was it difficult to have empathy for the other coach?

Other players?

Your own players who maybe didn't play so well?

Where does your EMPATHY go when you get beat? Humiliated? Angry?

How do you maintain a spirit of EXCELLENCE without a spirit of EMPATHY?

How about when you are the slaughtering team? Where is your EMPATHY then? As an InSideOut Coach, how do you protect the honor of everyone competing?

Read Luke 23:32-34.

What do you notice about Jesus' compassion for others in the midst of them slaughtering him?

Do you believe this same compassion and empathy are accessible to us through the Holy Spirit or is this just scriptural verbiage?

Are you willing to pray that empathy will permeate your new understanding of competition?

POST GAME:

"Empathy is the lifeblood of a virtuous coach and the core of a virtuous program." Page 227.

What action step can you take toward helping your team be a virtuous program?

What action step can you take to redefine competition for yourself, your players, other coaches and parents?

What action step will you take today to begin striving for mutual excellence in sports?

TRANSFORMATIONAL PRINCIPLE:

InSideOut Coaches are fueled by empathy, freed from a win-lose mentality and compete to honor the quest for excellence.

MEMORY VERSE:

"Whatever you do, do it enthusiastically, as something done for the Lord and not for people, knowing that you will receive the reward of an inheritance from the Lord - you serve the Lord Christ."
Colossians 3:23-24

"The relationships, the learning, the teaching and the coaching have all been one long, arduous, and ultimately liberating journey. The beauty of transformational coaching is that the transformation works both ways – it transforms us as coaches too. Our players teach us and challenge us. And if we listen, they tell us how to love them."
Page 251

PREGAME:

InSideOut Coaching Reading:

Chapter 10: pages 233-251

Themes to keep in mind: the purpose, meaning and power of ceremony, sports as part of every player's heroic journey, coaches as wise mentors to assist players along their journey.

Bible Readings:

I Corinthians 13:4-8a

Matthew 3:13-17

Luke 22:14-20

Themes to keep in mind: spirituality as self-transcendence, rites of passage, spiritual growth and connectivity through ceremony, parents as partners.

GAME PLAN:

Historically and globally every culture has recognized the need for transformative ceremony and rites of passage to acknowledge and confer the changed status of young people as they grow toward maturity and find their place in society. Transformational coaches use ceremonies in sports as tools, markers, and launching pads involving parents and community in this process.

WARM UP:

What was your reaction to Alex's letter at the beginning of Chapter 10?

Have you ever received a letter like that from a former player?

Did you notice how Alex signed his letter to Coach Ehrmann? Do you find that unusual or common language used by your players?

On page 246, Joe states, "All young people need to know three things before they graduate from high school."

What are the 3 things that all young people need to know?

1.

2.

3.

How do you define the word love? Are you comfortable with telling players you love them? Why or why not?

Joe and Biff teach their team the definition of love based on I Corinthians 13:4-8a. Study these verses and list the ways love can serves coaches, players, and a team.

GAME TIME:

In Joseph Campbell's classic, *The Hero with a Thousand Faces*, his "hero's journey" is a rite of passage that involves a five-step process. (page 236)

List the 5 steps:

1.

2.

3.

4.

5.

Where do you see young athletes experiencing this process? Do you?

In Luke 22:14-20 Jesus creates a "ceremony" for His players to help them remember the lessons He taught and modeled. How did this help prepare His team for challenges awaiting them?

Can you think of other ways that Jesus, as wise-mentor coach, prepared His team to handle life's challenges involving ceremony or rite of passage?

Joe states they uses ceremonies to bring players into the spiritual realm of sports encompassing beauty, transcendence and joy.

Write about a time when sport and ceremony have been connected for you?

Joe finishes the book back where he started, connecting the end back to the beginning. He declares that "the painful parts of my life were not an enemy to hide from. They were not something to deny, ignore, or repress. They were to be explored, understood from an adult perspective, and integrated into my life story." (page 249) As you think of your personal history, what memories or experiences have you reexamined and are starting to integrate as a result of this study?

POST GAME:

As Jesus begins to launch His public ministry, God, initiates a ceremony involving His personal and public affirmation of Jesus. Read Matthew 3:16-17.

What is the significance of this "ceremony?"

What three things did God say to Jesus and what is their significance to Jesus and the crowd?

1.

2.

3.

Imagine how the world would change if every player personally and publicly heard those words from his or her father and from his or her coach? How does your coaching demonstrate these three affirmations to your players?

Read pages 246-247 and compare Joe's experience at Georgetown with his son Barney and compare God the Father and His Son's ceremony in the Matthew 3 passage. How did Joe use this passage to create this "ceremony?"

List any kind of "ceremony" to signify the "rite of passage" you use to affirm accomplishments and the lessons learned from the heroic journey after a season playing for you.

If you were inclined to implement a couple of Joe and Biff's ceremonies or variations of them, which would they be and why?

What would be the potential obstacles?

What action steps will you take to deal with the obstacles?

Describe how you might change or improve your current ceremonies:

One coach having read InSideOut Coaching, prepared parents and players to implement ceremony into his closing banquet for the first time. He summed up the experience by saying, “Usually the best news about our banquet is that it is over (!), but last night was quite meaningful and a lot of fun to be a part of.”

TRANSFORMATIONAL PRINCIPLE:

InSideOut coaches use ceremony as a sacred process and passage to insure lessons taught are caught and to release their players to be agents of transformation for the rest of their lives.

Memory Verse:

“Not that I have already reached the goal or am already fully mature, but I make every effort to take hold of that for which Christ Jesus took hold of me.”
Philippians 3:13

"Love the Lord, your God, with all your heart, soul, mind and strength and love your neighbor, as yourself."
Jesus

"Integration (the linkage of differentiated elements of a system) might be the principle underlying health at all levels of our experience; from the microcosm of our inner world to our interpersonal relationships and life in our communities"
"Mindsight" by Daniel Siegel (page 68)

Be present in every moment with all that you have been given!
Paula Ehrmann

PREGAME:

Bible Readings:

Hebrews 13:15-16:

I Samuel 15:1-23:

Isaiah 1:10-17:

Micah 6:6-8:

Mark 7:5-7:

Romans 12:1-2:

Themes to keep in mind: Worship as a primary vocation for all believers. Worship as honoring, adoring, serving, and thanking God. Worship as upward and outward, individual and corporate, acceptable and unacceptable. Coaching can and should be considered an act of worship. Coaching, as an act of worship requires a mindful presence that allows the Spirit of God to actively work through us at all times, under all circumstances, in and out of season.

GAME PLAN:

The phrase, *What would Jesus do* has become trendy. Plastic refrigerator magnets and latex bracelets bearing the letters *WWJD* can cheapen the authentic integration of Jesus' moral imperatives to our coaching like demonstrating our love of Christ through purposeful, directed and conscious coaching. Jesus, as the epitome and model of the transformational coach, shows us how to live, love and transform lives as daily acts of worship to God. Jesus is our model of God manifested through man via the indwelling of the Holy Spirit. Jesus shows us how to live and coach in Godly presence – a state of worshipful gratitude.

Jesus did not have a game face and a private face. He had one face – one goal. He had one piece of business on which he had to focus – God's. And wherever Jesus went, He was totally present to both people and to His purpose. He placed His focus on doing his ultimate good in every moment, in every circumstance. Always. Jesus was, and is, an InSideOut Coach. He modeled transformational coaching by maintaining a consistent, integrated and purposeful presentation of His relationship to God, regardless of how much He was pushed, pulled, squeezed, tortured and tormented.

We believe that the reason you have gotten this far in the process is because you know that this capacity to be a godly presence for your players, fellow coaches and families is within you. We have spent 12 sessions together, studying, journaling, sharing, praying and learning about ourselves, and God's common calling for us to be impact players in others' lives. We have touched on many areas that will require greater study, deeper practice and lots of patience. There will be rocky roads and times of discouragement as well as moments of glorious victory. Partnering with fellow Transformational Coaches is encouraged and will be very helpful in supporting you as you build your program. Kindness and empathy along this road are as critical to have for yourself as they are for you to have for others. Review your notes regularly and prepare yourself daily to coach in a way that demonstrates your personal growth.

In this sessions study, and in concluding this part of our journey together, we examine how worship looks when it is integrated into our day-to day living, 24/7, 168 hours a week and to each and every moment of our coaching experience.

WARM UP:

How do you define worship?

Have you ever thought of coaching as worshipping?

Do you find it easy being the same person in every environment or do you find that environments tend to dictate your beliefs and your behaviors?

GAME TIME:

Read Hebrews 13:15-16.

There are two complementary aspects of worship in these verses. One involves a redeemed heart, and the other, redeemed hands, praise and practice.

What are they?

1.

2.

How do they manifest themselves in your coaching?

Do you feel your coaching is pleasing to God?

Coaching Point: Coaching, as an act of worship is u ____________________________

to God and o ____________________________ to our players.

Read 1 Samuel 15:1-23

How does Saul disobey God in verses 9, 12?

Have you ever been tempted to make your team or win-lose record a testimony to your own honor as opposed to God working in and through you?

What principle of worship does Samuel teach Saul in verses 22-23?

Is your coaching obedient to God's Word and His desires for you and your players?

Coaching point: O ______________________________ is an indispensable part of worship.

Read Isaiah 1:10-17

All that God ordained as ingredients of Old Testament worship are seen in these verses: sacrifices, offerings, incense, feasts, festivals, choirs of prayers and praise. Yet God rejects their worship with very harsh words.

Why, do you think?

What worship curriculum and action steps does God ask of His people?

Give some examples of similar teachings in Joe and Biff's curriculum from our lessons in InSideOut Coaching, (or examples from your own transformational coaching experiences):

Coaching Point: Righteous living that produces and maintains God's Justice in the world and upholds the inherent value of every player must precede rites of worship or God will not accept them.

New Testament Transition: Old Testament animal sacrifice has culminated in the once-for-all sacrifice of Christ on the Cross. While the Old Testament principles of worship remain, Paul expands on these and declares that all of who we are, and all of what we do, is the content of our worship. All of our humanity and all of our relationships are brought to worship.

Read Mark 7:5-8

Jesus calls these false worshippers hypocrites. Why?

Is your coaching based on spiritual principals or the secular traditions of coaching?

Coaching Point: Worship prescribed by human traditions rather than the Word of God is vain and unacceptable to God.

Read Romans 12:1-2

"Therefore, as Paul writes, refers to his previous 11 chapters in Romans, meaning, now that we are in Christ and Christ is in us, we are to offer our bodies as a living sacrifice, holy and pleasing to God."

Notice Paul does not say offer your Spirit but our, bodies as a living sacrifice.

What do you think Paul means by this?

Would you define your coaching as a "living sacrifice?"

What part of our coaching is to be offered to Christ?

"Do not conform."

Paul is telling us to not let worship be squeezed out of our coaching.

Share the pressures you feel as a coach to compartmentalize your spiritual beliefs from your coaching:

"...but be transformed by the renewing of your mind then you will be able to test and approve what God's will is—his good, pleasing and perfect will."

Why renew your mind?

POST GAME:

Coaching Point: Be present in every moment with all that you have been given.

Write down three action steps you will take to integrate your coaching and your worship into one practice:

1.

2.

3.

How will the spiritual disciplines play a role in renewing your coaching mindset?

TRANSFORMATIONAL PRINCIPLE:

InSideOut Coaches present their coaching to the Lordship of Christ as a daily act of worship as we live, love and coach our players with renewed minds that are pleasing and acceptable to God.

MEMORY VERSE:

"Therefore, I urge you, brothers and sisters, in view of God's mercy, to offer your bodies as living sacrifices, holy and pleasing to God—this is your spiritual act of worship. Do not conform any longer to the pattern of this world, but be transformed by the renewing of your mind. Then you will be able to test and approve what God's will is—his good, pleasing and perfect will."

Romans 12:1-2

JOE EHRMANN, educator, author, activist, ordained minister and coach for more than 25 years, was an All-American football player at Syracuse University, lettered in lacrosse and was selected to the Syracuse All-Century Football Team. Joe went on to play professional football for 13 years. Joe's passion for transforming the culture of sports and his revolutionary concepts of transformational coaching, teambuilding and mentoring led Parade Magazine to feature him on its cover, naming him ***The Most Important Coach in America.*** In addition, the Institute for International Sport selected him as one of the ***Most Influential Sport Educators in America.*** Joe received his formal theological training at Dallas Theological Seminary and Westminster Theological Seminary.

PAULA EHRMANN is a licensed, clinical, professional counselor with over 20 years experience. Through her private practice, PeachTherapy and, as CEO of Coach for America, Paula works with individuals and couples, therapeutically, as well as with community and corporate groups to transform personal beliefs, values and public practices.

Married for over 35 years, **Joe and Paula** have built a uniquely impactful message they are delivering across the country, stressing the value of relationships and a commitment to making a difference in the world.

Visit **Joe and Paula** at www.coachforamerica.com

MARK HULL serves as the Wisconsin State Director for the Fellowship of Christian Athletes. In his 24th year on FCA staff, Mark is a former teacher and coach who also served as a missionary in the Philippines where he met his wife Marcel. When they tell you missions experience changes your life, he'll vouch for that!

Acknowledgements

A special thanks to Ralph Mierow, Rick Mathison, Jeff Tarras, Steve Collins and Andrew Draper, the FCA staff team in Wisconsin who all had a hand in the development of this study. This WI team would like to extend our gratitude to a truly transformational teammate Wayne "Butch" Preston whose gift of encouragement makes everyone in his path feel like the most important person in the world.